The
Substance Abuse
& Recovery
Workbook

Self-Assessments, Exercises
& Educational Handouts

John J. Liptak, EdD
Ester A. Leutenberg

Illustrated by
Amy L. Brodsky, LISW

Whole Person Associates
Duluth, Minnesota

Whole Person Associates
210 West Michigan Street
Duluth, MN 55802-1908

800-247-6789

books@wholeperson.com
www.wholeperson.com

The Substance Abuse & Recovery Workbook
Self-Assessments, Exercises & Educational Handouts

Printed in the United States of America

10 9 8 7 6 5 4 3 2 1

Editorial Director: Carlene Sippola
Art Director: Joy Morgan Dey

Library of Congress Control Number: 2007942422
ISBN: 978-1-57025-225-9

Using This Book *(For the professional)*

Substance abuse has no universally accepted definition. Substance abuse refers to the use of substances in ways outside of societal conventions and that have an adverse effect on an individual. Other terms associated with substance abuse include chemical dependency, drug addiction, drug abuse, and substance dependence. Any use of drugs in a manner that violates the norms of society is considered substance abuse. In the fourth edition of the Diagnostic and Statistical Manual of Mental Disorders (DSM-IV), the American Psychological Association defines substance abuse as . . .

A maladaptive pattern of substance use leading to clinically significant impairment or distress, as manifested by one or more of the following, occurring within a twelve month period of time:

> *1) Recurrent substance use resulting in a failure to fulfill major role obligations at work, school, or home (e.g., repeated absences or poor work performance related to substance abuse; substance-related absences, suspensions or expulsions from school; neglect of children or household).*
>
> *2) Recurrent substance use in situations in which it is physically hazardous (e.g., driving an automobile or operating a machine when impaired by substance use).*
>
> *3) Recurrent substance-related legal problems (e.g., arrests for substance-related disorderly conduct).*
>
> *4) Continued substance use despite having persistent or recurrent social or interpersonal problem caused or exacerbated by the effects of the substance, e.g., arguments with spouse about consequences of intoxication, physical fights).*

Addictions come in many different shapes and forms. When most people hear the word addiction, they usually think of drug use and abuse. In reality, there are many different types of addictions that have very different effects on the body and mind of the abuser. Some of the different types of addictions include:

Drug and alcohol – This is probably the most common of all of the addictions. It is estimated that there are approximately twenty million people in the United States who suffer from the abuse of alcohol and certain drugs. Common among these include LSD, Speed, PCP, Steroids, and prescription drugs.

Caffeine – Many people do not even see this as an addiction. However, caffeine is a stimulant that many people consume in vast quantities on a daily basis.

Cigarettes and cigars – Tobacco today is one of the most popular as well as most problematic of all of the addictions. Nicotine has been proven to be a very powerful, highly addictive drug.

Computers – Because our society has become so dependent on different types of technology, computers can become very addictive. Computers were designed to help people reduce their workweek by making work easier, but people are actually spending so much time using a computer that they have become dependent on them and suffer withdrawal when they are unable to use them.

Gambling – As the opportunities become increasingly available to gamble, so does the number of people who are addicted to gambling. As gambling is seen on television, available on the Internet, and now available in many states, people are increasingly becoming addicted to the risks involved in gambling.

There are many other types of addictions including sexual, eating, and shopping to name a few. Although this book is geared toward people suffering from substance abuse issues, many of the pages might be applicable to populations suffering from some of the other addictions. You will need to use your clinical judgment in determining whether the assessments and activities will be effective for the population with whom you work. There may be some handouts you will not use because they do not fit the needs of your population. If your clients are working on other programs, such as AA, you will need to make sure that the exercises and journaling activities do not conflict with your program objectives.

The Substance Abuse & Recovery Workbook contains five separate sections that will help the participants learn more about themselves as well how substance abuse is impacting their lives.

- **Substance Abuse Scale** helps individuals to determine the level of their addiction to drug and/or alcohol, and the nature of their addiction.

- **Addictive Personality Scale** helps individuals examine if they have a constellation of personality traits that predisposes them to various addictions.

- **Codependency Characteristics Scale** helps individuals measure how well they fulfill the normal responsibilities of adult life, how they can identify their feelings of inadequacy, and leads them to explore things that are lacking in their life.

- **Relapse Warning Signs Scale** helps individuals identify the changes in thinking, feeling and behavior that accompany relapse.

- **Substance Abuse Cessation Scale** helps individuals get a clearer picture of the excuses that they may be using to continue their abuse of substances.

These sections serve as an avenue for individual self-reflection, as well as group experiences revolving around identified topics of importance. Each assessment includes directions for easy administration, scoring and interpretation. Values of these self-assessments are, they . . .

- take into account life experiences of different clients.

- take into account similarities across cultures and unique aspects of cultures that may possibly be influencing members of the culture.

- recognize but do not pathologize people from different cultures.

- respect norms established for populations similar to those with whom you are working.

- serve as non-threatening measures.

Each section includes exploratory activities, reflective journaling exercises and educational handouts to help participants discover their habitual and ineffective methods of managing substance abuse, and to explore new ways for bringing about healing.

In the past twenty years, many research studies have focused on the value of self-reflection and journaling as a way of exploring personal characteristics, identifying ineffective behaviors and examining thoughts and feelings that lead to ineffective behaviors. This book is unique with its combination of two powerful psychological tools for substance abuse and recovery management: self-assessment and journaling.

(Using This Book continued)

The art of self-reflection goes back many centuries and is rooted in many of the world's greatest spiritual and philosophical traditions. Socrates, the ancient Greek philosopher, was known to walk the streets engaging the people he met in philosophical reflection and dialogue. He felt that this type of activity was so important in life that he proclaimed, "The unexamined life is not worth living!" The unexamined life is one in which the same routine is continually repeated without ever thinking about its meaning to one's life and how this life really could be lived. However, a *structured* reflection and examination of beliefs, assumptions, characteristics and patterns can provide a better understanding which can lead to a more satisfying personal life and career. A greater level of self-understanding about important life skills is often necessary to make positive, self-directed changes from the negative patterns that keep repeating throughout life. The assessments and exercises in this book can help promote this self-understanding. Through involvement in the in-depth activities, the participant claims ownership in the development of positive patterns.

Journaling is an extremely powerful tool for enhancing self-discovery, learning, transcending traditional problems, breaking ineffective lifestyle and career habits, and helping to heal from past psychological traumas. From a physical point of view, writing reduces feelings of stress and lowers muscle tension, and writing lowers blood pressure and heart rate levels. Psychologically, writing reduces feelings of sadness, depression and general anxiety, and leads to a greater level of life satisfaction and optimism. Behaviorally, the journaling leads to enhanced social skills, emotional intelligence and creativity.

By combining reflective assessment and journaling, your participants will engage in a revolutionary method for reducing and managing their substance abuse issues.

Thanks to the following professionals whose input in this book has been invaluable!

Nancy Day, OT Reg (Ont.)

Amy Herzenstein, M.Ed.

Kathy Khalsa, OTR/L

Kathy Liptak, Ed.D.

Eileen Regen, M.Ed., CJE

Karal Stern, LISW, LICDC

The Assessments, Journaling Activities, and Educational Handouts

The Assessments, Journaling Activities, and Educational Handouts in this book are reproducible and ready to be photocopied for participants' use. The assessments in this book focus on self-reported data and are similar to ones used by psychologists, counselors, and career consultants. The accuracy and usefulness of the information provided is dependent on the truthful information that each participant provides about him / herself. By being honest, participants help themselves to learn about unproductive and ineffective patterns, and to uncover information that might be keeping them from being as happy and / or as successful as they can be.

An assessment instrument can provide participants with valuable information about themselves; however, it cannot measure or identify everything about themselves. Its purpose is not to pigeon-hole certain characteristics, but rather to allow them to explore all of their characteristics. This book contains informal assessments and not tests. Tests measure knowledge or whether something is right or wrong. For the assessments in this book, there are no right or wrong answers. These assessments only ask for personal opinions or attitudes about a topic of importance in the participant's career and life.

When administering the assessments in this workbook, remember that the items are generically written so that they will be applicable to a wide variety of people but will not account for every possible variable for every person. None of the assessments are specifically tailored to one person, so use the assessments to help participants identify negative themes in their lives and find ways to break the hold that these patterns and their effects have in life.

Advise the participants taking the assessments that they should not spend too much time trying to analyze the content of the questions; they should think about the questions in general and then spontaneously report how they feel about each one. Whatever the results of the assessment, encourage participants to talk about their findings and their feelings about what they discovered about themselves.

Writing and talking about substance abuse and recovery issues is therapeutic for most people.

Layout of the Book

The Substance Abuse & Recovery Workbook is designed to be used either independently or as part of an integrated curriculum. You may administer one of the assessments and the journaling exercises to an individual or a group with whom you are working, or you may administer a number of the assessments over one or more days.

This book includes five sections, each of which contains:

- **Assessment Instruments** — Self-assessment inventories with scoring directions and interpretation materials. Group facilitators can choose one or more of the activities relevant to their participants.

- **Activity Handouts** — Practical questions and activities that prompt self-reflection and promote self-understanding. These questions and activities foster introspection and promote pro-social behaviors.

- **Reflective Questions for Journaling** — Self-exploration activities and journaling exercises specific to each assessment to enhance self-discovery, learning, and healing.

- **Educational Handouts** — Handouts designed to enhance instruction can be used individually or in groups to enhance recovery from substance abuse and provide positive reinforcement for continued health and wellness. They can be distributed, converted into masters for overheads or transparencies, or written down on a board and discussed.

Who should use this program?

This book has been designed as a practical tool for helping professionals, such as therapists, counselors, psychologists, teachers, and group leaders. Depending on the role of the professional using *The Substance Abuse & Recovery Workbook* and the specific client or group's needs, these sections can be used individually, combined or as part of an integrated curriculum, for a more comprehensive approach.

Why use self-assessments?

Self-assessments are important in teaching various substance abuse management skills because they help participants . . .

- Become aware of the primary motivators that guide their behavior
- Explore and learn to *let go* of troublesome habits and behavioral patterns learned in childhood
- Explore the effects of unconscious childhood messages
- Gain insight and *a wake up call* for behavioral change
- Focus their thinking on behavioral goals for change
- Uncover resources they possess that can help them to cope better with problems and difficulties
- Explore their personal characteristics without judgment
- Develop full awareness of their strengths and weaknesses

Because the assessments are presented in a straightforward and easy-to-use format, individuals can self-administer, score and interpret each assessment at their own pace.

Introduction for the Participant

Substance abuse refers to an over-indulgence in, and a dependence on, a variety of addictive substances including cigarettes, alcohol, illegal drugs, prescription drugs, and smokeless tobacco. People abuse these types of substances for a variety of complicated reasons, but primarily because they like the way they feel when they are using them. Pleasure can be a motivating force in your life and your body and brain are wired to continue doing things that feel good. Thus, all addictive drugs can affect and be affected by your system's natural need to keep doing things that feel good.

An addiction is a disease that negatively affects your emotions, thinking and behavior. Once you begin to use addictive substances, their effect on your brain and body will make you want to continue using them. You will know that you have a substance abuse problem if you continue to use substances even though they cause problems in your relationships, at home or at school, in the workplace, with money, with the law, or with your health. You also may have a problem if you need to keep using more and more of the substance to get the same effect.

The good news is that if you feel as if you have a problem, the assessments and journaling activities included in this book can help you commit to a plan to ensure that you break the addictive habit.

The Substance Abuse & Recovery Workbook relies on a self- reflective method that is both therapeutic and fun. Self-realization through journaling enables you to deeply understand your addictions and how your body and mind has become used to behaving. This strong insight through reflective journaling then allows you the opportunity to use the exercises in this book to break the addictive cycle and form new habits and behaviors toward an addiction-free life

This book is designed to help you learn about substance abuse and addictions in your life and make constructive changes to better manage the addictions that have taken hold of your life, relationships and career.

TABLE OF CONTENTS

TABLE OF CONTENTS

TABLE OF CONTENTS

SECTION I:
Substance Abuse Scale

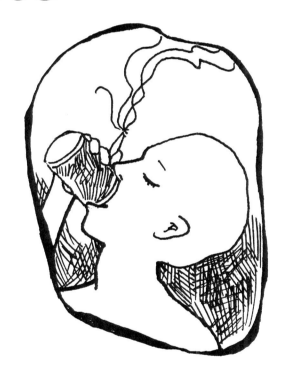

Name_____

Date_____

Substance Abuse Scale Directions

The Substance Abuse Scale can help you determine the level of your addiction to drugs and/or alcohol, and the nature of your addiction. This scale contains 32 statements. Read each of the statements and decide whether or not the statement describes you. In each of the choices listed, circle the number of your response on the line to the right of each statement.

4 = Very Much Like Me	3 = Usually Like Me	2 = Somewhat Like Me	1 = Not Like Me

In the following example, the circled 4 indicates the statement is very much like the person completing the scale.

1. I am sick or feel physically bad most of the time . . . . (4)   3   2   1

This is not a test, and there are no right or wrong answers. Do not spend too much time thinking about your answers. Your initial response will likely be the most true for you. Be sure to respond to every statement.

(Turn to the next page and begin)

Substance Abuse Scale

4 = Very Much Like Me	**3 = Usually Like Me**	**2 = Somewhat Like Me**	**1 = Not Like Me**

	4	3	2	1
1. I am sick or feel physically bad most of the time	4	3	2	1
2. I have difficulty in thinking, remembering, and doing things I used to be able to do	4	3	2	1
3. I often give up on things in my life	4	3	2	1
4. I have problems working and keeping a job	4	3	2	1
5. Sometimes I can't remember what has happened to me	4	3	2	1
6. I can't make decisions about things, so I just wait to see what happens	4	3	2	1
7. Nothing else matters in my life except getting and using	4	3	2	1
8. I want a Higher Power to save me from my addictions	4	3	2	1
9. It often takes stronger alcohol / drugs to get the same effect	4	3	2	1
10. I change jobs, move or leave relationships a lot	4	3	2	1
11. I often feel alone and lost	4	3	2	1
12. I cannot control or quit my use of substances	4	3	2	1
13. I hang around other people who use as much or more than I do	4	3	2	1
14. I often avoid family and friends unless I need something	4	3	2	1
15. I do not want to take the necessary steps to get better	4	3	2	1
16. I get pushy or show off around other people	4	3	2	1
17. I make excuses for my drug and alcohol use	4	3	2	1
18. I hide and sneak drugs so people will not know how much I use	4	3	2	1

(Continued on the next page)

© 2008 WHOLE PERSON ASSOCIATES, 210 WEST MICHIGAN ST., DULUTH MN 55802-1908 ▪ 800-247-6789

(Substance Abuse Scale continued)

	4 = Very Much Like Me	3 = Usually Like Me	2 = Somewhat Like Me	1 = Not Like Me
19. I feel afraid and I am on guard all the time	4	3	2	1
20. I make promises but have trouble keeping them.	4	3	2	1
21. It takes me much less time to get high than it used to	4	3	2	1
22. I get into trouble when I use alcohol / drugs.	4	3	2	1
23. I feel angry and resentful a lot of the time.	4	3	2	1
24. I rarely do anything that does not involve my addictions	4	3	2	1
25. I do things that I never thought I would do	4	3	2	1
26. I don't eat the proper foods or eat at a regular time	4	3	2	1
27. I feel guilty about using and the things I do when I use	4	3	2	1
28. I don't listen when other people try to talk with me about my addictions	4	3	2	1
29. I would often use with other people who were worse off than me so I could feel better about myself	4	3	2	1
30. I get the shakes, sweats, or feel terrible unless I drink or use drugs	4	3	2	1
31. I feel bad about how my using hurts other people, but I can't stop my behavior	4	3	2	1
32. I use drugs and alcohol to cope with my problems	4	3	2	1
33. Substances are more important than anything in life	4	3	2	1
34. I sometimes carry drugs or alcohol around with me	4	3	2	1
35. I create situations (parties, attending bars) in which I can use substances	4	3	2	1
36. I sometimes wonder if life just isn't worth living	4	3	2	1

(Go to the Scoring Directions on the next page)

Substance Abuse Scale
Scoring Directions

The Substance Abuse Scale is designed to measure your level of addiction to various substances. Four areas have been identified to make up the scales for this assessment: Physical, Behavioral, Emotional, and Psychological. The items that make up each of the four scales are grouped so that you can explore how your addictions are showing themselves. To score your Substance Abuse Scale:

1. Record each of the scores from the previous two pages on the lines below. For example, if you circled the 4 for item number 1, you would put a 4 on the line above the 1 on the chart below. Do the same for all 36 items.

2. Add the totals for each of the 4 rows and put that total on the total line to the right.

___	___	___	___	___	___	___	___	___	_____
1	5	9	13	17	21	25	29	33	Physical Total

___	___	___	___	___	___	___	___	___	_____
2	6	10	14	18	22	26	30	34	Behavioral Total

___	___	___	___	___	___	___	___	___	_____
3	7	11	15	19	23	27	31	35	Emotional Total

___	___	___	___	___	___	___	___	___	_____
4	8	12	16	20	24	28	32	36	Psychological Total

The Profile Interpretation section on the next page can help you interpret your scores on the Substance Abuse Scale.

Interpretation of the Substance Abuse Scale

The remainder of the assessment contains interpretation materials to help determine if you are addicted to drugs and/or alcohol. This scale can help you to identify whether your addiction is primarily Physical, Behavioral, Emotional, and / or Psychological in nature.

Substance Abuse Scale Profile Interpretation

TOTAL SCORES FOR EACH OF THE FOUR SCALES	RESULT	INDICATIONS
28 to 36	High	You are probably experiencing many of the difficulties associated with substance use and abuse.
18 to 27	Moderate	You are probably experiencing some difficulties associated with substance use and abuse.
9 to 17	Low	You are probably not experiencing many of the difficulties associated with substance use and abuse.

For scales which you scored in the **Moderate** or **High** range, find the descriptions on the pages that follow. Then, read the description and complete the exercises that are included. No matter how you scored, low, moderate or high, you will benefit from these exercises.

Scale Descriptions

PHYSICAL – People who are addicted to substances fail to take adequate care of themselves because they are preoccupied with their addiction. They may not get enough sleep, take unnecessary risks, often skip meals and do not eat a proper diet. They often feel bad physically and start to find themselves making excuses while they are using various substances. They find that it often takes stronger substances to get the same effects they had been getting, and that they can get high in less time than usual. They find themselves starting to forget things and often find themselves doing things they never thought they would. Substances rapidly become the most important thing in their lives.

BEHAVIORAL – People who are addicted to substances have difficulty maintaining relationships with others. They often lose their sense of self and their connection to others. In addition, they may start to have trouble at work or in school. They find themselves beginning to have trouble making decisions and completing tasks. They find themselves frequently changing jobs and leaving relationships. They find themselves avoiding friends and family who may find out about their addiction. They often begin to hide substances and sneak to use them so people do not know how much they are using. They also find themselves feeling bad and shaking when they are not using.

EMOTIONAL – People who are addicted to substances generally have low self-esteem. They tend to experience feelings such as anxiety, fear, guilt, depression and shame. They tend to have unexplained mood swings and are likely to have episodes of anger and rage. At times they will even be violent with others around them. They often feel like they are not good at anything but using substances. They sometimes feel alone, lost and afraid. They feel angry and resentful, and then feel bad about the effect that their using has on people around them.

PSYCHOLOGICAL – People addicted to substances often experience difficulty in their thinking. They tend to have impaired reasoning and judgment. They are often unable to think things through logically. Their impaired thinking affects their performance on the job. They refuse to listen to other people who are talking with them about their addiction. Because they have difficulty coping with problems while they are addicted, they use substances to help them cope with the stresses of life. They often have such difficulty in reasoning and in coping with life's problems, they wonder if life is worth living.

The next sections are some self-reflective questions to help you overcome your addictions. Please complete the questions and journaling exercises on the following pages.

Problems in Your Life

Most experts feel that substance abuse is a physical disease similar to heart disease. It is a disease that causes you to be addicted to the use of alcohol or other drugs. This addiction causes you a variety of physical, emotional, relationship, school, college, career and spiritual problems.

How has substance abuse caused problems for you…

With your family?

_____

_____

_____

_____

With your friends?

_____

_____

_____

_____

In your social life?

_____

_____

_____

_____

At work? School? University?

_____

_____

_____

_____

(Problems in Your Life continued)

How has substance abuse caused problems for you...

With your health?

_____

_____

_____

_____

With your finances?

_____

_____

_____

_____

With the law and courts?

_____

_____

_____

_____

Other?

_____

_____

_____

_____

Self-Defeating Behaviors

When I am abusing substance I . . .

_____

_____

_____

_____

_____

_____

When I think about myself as an addict, I feel . . .

_____

_____

_____

_____

_____

_____

Self-defeating behaviors I exhibit when I abuse substances . . .

_____

_____

_____

_____

_____

_____

Addictive Life History

Please complete the following sentence starters to better understand the developmental history of your substance use:

As a child, I....

_____

_____

_____

In elementary school, I...

_____

_____

_____

In middle school, I...

_____

_____

_____

In high school, I...

_____

_____

_____

In college / university, I...

_____

_____

_____

As an adult, I...

_____

_____

_____

When You Were Using

Things you liked about yourself:

_____

_____

_____

Things you did not like about yourself:

_____

_____

_____

What benefits did you receive from alcohol and drug use?

_____

_____

_____

What did you think drugs and alcohol would do to help you?

_____

_____

_____

What things did you believe drugs and alcohol could help you stop doing?

_____

_____

_____

Non-Addicted People

People who do not have addictive thoughts, feelings and behaviors demonstrate several important traits. By answering the following questions, you will be able to explore your own addictive behaviors.

Non-Addictive People . . .

1) Face their problems head on

How do you avoid or try to avoid your problems?

_____

_____

_____

_____

_____

_____

2) Recognize their limitations

What are your limitations?

_____

_____

_____

_____

_____

_____

(Continued on the next page)

(Non-Addicted People continued)

3) Set realistic goals

What are your short-term goals (for the next month or so)?

_____

_____

_____

_____

_____

_____

What are your long-range goals (within the next six motnhs)?

_____

_____

_____

_____

_____

_____

4) Appreciate their strengths

What are your strengths?

_____

_____

_____

_____

_____

_____

(Continued on the next page)

(Non-Addicted People continued)

5) Have a hopeful and positive outlook on life

How would you describe your life outlook and why?

_____

_____

_____

_____

_____

_____

6) Are spontaneous and creative

In what positive ways have you shown spontaneity in your life?

_____

_____

_____

_____

_____

_____

In what positive ways have you expressed your creativity in your life?

_____

_____

_____

_____

_____

_____

Learning About Habits

What have you learned about your substance abuse habits?

_____

_____

_____

_____

_____

_____

_____

_____

_____

_____

_____

_____

_____

_____

_____

_____

_____

_____

_____

_____

_____

_____

_____

_____

Feeling Scared

What scares you about using?

_____

_____

_____

_____

_____

_____

_____

_____

_____

_____

What scares you about not using?

_____

_____

_____

_____

_____

_____

_____

_____

_____

_____

_____

_____

Feeling Pain

How have your substance abuse habits caused you pain over the years?

_____

_____

_____

_____

_____

_____

_____

_____

_____

_____

_____

_____

_____

_____

_____

_____

_____

_____

_____

_____

_____

_____

Signs of Addictive Behavior

- You can never get enough and constantly feel the need to get more.

- You do not get pleasure from the behavior.

- You have a lower sense of self-esteem because of the behavior.

- You feel like a failure because of the behavior.

- You are inflexible when it comes to the behavior.

- You feel driven to engage in the behavior.

Denial That Addiction Exists

People are in denial about addictions when they . . .

- Admit they have a problem but do not take the necessary steps to change.

- Blame others for their mistakes.

- Make excuses whenever possible.

- Get angry if someone brings up the subject of addictions.

- Distance themselves from the addiction by refusing to talk about it.

- Insist that they will have no problem quitting or decreasing their use.

- Saying the can stop whenever they want.

- If they do quit, insisting that they will have no problem staying sober / abstinent, without support.

SECTION II:
Addictive Personality Scale

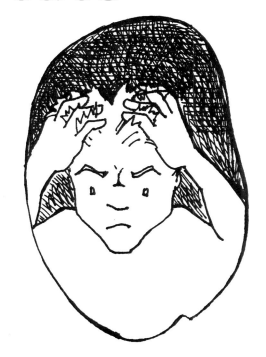

Name_____

Date_____

Addictive Personality Scale Directions

An addiction is often defined as an abnormal relationship with an object like tobacco or alcohol, an event like watching television or surfing the Internet, or a behavior like shoplifting or gambling. An addiction often begins as a pleasurable activity in which you voluntarily engage, but ends in compulsion, a loss of control of your actions, and the need to repeat the action even though it may be harmful to you. The Addictive Personality Scale was designed to help you examine if you have a cluster of personality traits that predispose you to various addictions.

This assessment contains 40 statements related to your personality. Read each of the statements and decide whether or not the statement describes you. If the statement is **TRUE**, circle the number next to that item under the **TRUE** column. If the statement is **FALSE**, circle the number next to that item under the **FALSE** column.

In the following example, the circled number under **FALSE** indicates the statement is not true of the person completing the inventory.

	TRUE	**FALSE**
I have a general lack of confidence	2	(1)

This is not a test, and there are no right or wrong answers. Do not spend too much time thinking about your answers. Your initial response will likely be the most true for you.

Be sure to respond to every statement.

(Turn to the next page and begin)

Addictive Personality Scale

	TRUE	FALSE
(A) I have a general lack of confidence	1	2
(A) My self-esteem is as good as most other people	2	1
(A) I feel powerless and victimized	1	2
(A) Personal criticism does not bother me	2	1
(A) I do not need the approval of others	2	1
(A) I try to please others most of the time	1	2
(A) I often feel inferior to other people	1	2
(A) I am not concerned about what others think of me	2	1
(A) I have felt inferior to others since my childhood	1	2
(A) I would not consider myself conforming or compliant	2	1
(B) I often feel alienated from other people	1	2
(B) I often do what my peers or colleagues want me to do	1	2
(B) I am good at developing trusting relationships	2	1
(B) My interpersonal communication skills are effective	2	1
(B) I have trouble talking with other people	1	2
(B) I have trouble seeking comfort from others	1	2
(B) I am rarely susceptible to peer pressure	2	1
(B) I have trouble connecting with other people	1	2
(B) I have trouble developing interpersonal relationships	1	2
(B) I enjoy deep involvement with others	2	1

(Continued on the next page)

(Addictive Personality Scale continued)

	TRUE	FALSE
(C) I often feel overwhelmed by my problems	1	2
(C) I have effective problem-solving skills	2	1
(C) I have trouble setting realistic goals	1	2
(C) I usually will do anything to avoid conflict	1	2
(C) I usually feel uncertain about the future	1	2
(C) I know and use a variety of methods for dealing with stress	2	1
(C) I rarely ignore or run away from my problems	2	1
(C) I find myself jumping from job to job	1	2
(C) I do not deal well with frustration	1	2
(C) I often am creative and spontaneous	2	1
(D) I get bored easily	1	2
(D) I am an effective risk-taker	2	1
(D) I am rarely impulsive	2	1
(D) I have hyperactive levels of energy	1	2
(D) I constantly search for exciting or stimulating activities	1	2
(D) I turn to an addiction to relieve my boredom	1	2
(D) I rarely take unnecessary risks	2	1
(D) Through my addiction I feel a sense of excitement	1	2
(D) I have a need for instant gratification	1	2
(D) I like to live on the edge	1	2

(Go to the Scoring Directions on the next page)

Addictive Personality Scale
Scoring Directions

The Addictive Personality Scale is designed to measure whether or not you possess an addictive personality. To get your Self-Esteem score, total the numbers that you circled for the statements marked (A) in the previous section. You will get a number from 10 to 20. Put that number in the space marked (A) SELF-ESTEEM TOTAL below. Then do the same for the other three scales – (B) Relationships, (C) Life Skills and (D) Excitement.

(A) SELF-ESTEEM TOTAL   =   _____

(B) RELATIONSHIPS TOTAL   =   _____

(C) LIFESKILLS TOTAL   =   _____

(D) EXCITEMENT TOTAL   =   _____

To get your overall addictive personality score, add the four scores above. Your overall score will range from 40 to 80. Put your total score in the space below:

ADDICTIVE PERSONALITY TOTAL = _____

Go to the next page to interpret your scores.

© 2008 WHOLE PERSON ASSOCIATES, 210 WEST MICHIGAN ST., DULUTH MN 55802-1908 • 800-247-6789

Addictive Personality Scale
Profile Interpretation

TOTAL INDIVIDUAL SCORES	TOTAL SCORE FOR ALL FOUR SCALES	RESULT	INDICATIONS
17 to 20	67 to 80	High	You do not show many of the tendencies of people with addictive personalities. A high score suggests that you tend to have high self-esteem, easily develop relationships with other people, have effective life skills and engage in satisfying leisure activities but do not constantly seek leisure activities that are too stimulating or destructive.
14 to 16	54 to 66	Moderate	You have a moderate addictive personality, one in which you have some tendencies to have an addictive personality, but not all of the time.
10 to 13	40 to 53	Low	You show many of the tendencies of people with addictive personalities. A low score suggests that you tend to have low self-esteem, often have difficulty developing effective relationships with other people, may lack appropriate life skills and often engage in leisure activities that are exciting and give you an adrenalin rush.

For scales which you scored in the **Moderate** or **High** range, find the descriptions on the pages that follow. Then, read the description and complete the exercises that are included. No matter how you scored, low, moderate or high, you will benefit from these exercises.

(Continued on the next page)

Addictive Personality Scale Descriptions

(A) SELF-ESTEEM

People scoring low on the Self-Esteem Scale have difficulty finding meaning in their lives. You might wonder why you need to get up in the morning. Because of your lack of self-esteem, you start to pull away from others and pull inside of yourself. You begin to feel a general lack of self-esteem, self-control and self-confidence. As you withdraw from other people, you slowly begin to become more attached to the object of your addiction.

(B) RELATIONSHIPS

People scoring low on the Relationship Scale have experienced unhealthy relationships in life. You probably have trouble trusting other people, were treated poorly as a child and have a difficult time creating a bond with other people. You may have been raised in a family where closeness was not available to you. You tend not to get too close to other people or develop intimate relationships. Perhaps you are currently trying to fill an empty void that you feel because of a lack of closeness in your family growing up. Addictions offer you the promise of filling the empty void you currently feel.

(C) LIFE SKILLS

People scoring low on the Life Skills Scale often lack the appropriate life skills needed to deal effectively with their predisposition to addictions. Because you have abandoned the socially acceptable ways of having your emotional needs met, you often have difficulty solving problems, communicating with others and dealing with stress in your life. You may not set achievable goals for yourself and are uncertain about your future. Important life skills you need to learn more about include ways to more effectively connect with others, develop a social support system, identify interests that lead to greater self-esteem and self-actualization, and integrating spirituality into your life.

(D) EXCITEMENT

People scoring low on the Excitement Scale often have a need to engage in exciting and stimulating leisure activities. It is through these types of activities that you get your "high." You tend to get bored very easily and then begin to search for activities that provide a sense of excitement. You are an extreme risk taker and will take risks regardless of the danger involved. You have high levels of energy for which you must find an outlet. You tend to be impulsive and most often seek instant gratification in your activities.

Regardless of your score on the Addictive Personality Scale, the following exercises have been designed to help you learn more about your personality and your predisposition to the addictive personality type. The exercises that follow are designed to help you to capitalize on your strengths and overcome your weaknesses.

Increasing Your Self-Esteem

The first secret in overcoming an addictive personality is to engage in those activities in which you have success, and thus high self-esteem. Begin by writing the things from your background or personal history that you have accomplished. These should be a source of pride for you.

Things I am most proud of from my work or school / university

Things I have accomplished	Why they provide me with a sense of pride

(Increasing Your Self-Esteem continued)

Things I am most proud of from my leisure or family activities

Things I have accomplished	Why they provide me with a sense of pride

Passions

People with addictive personalities often become obsessed with high-risk activities because they have not yet found their inner passions. Take a minute and answer the following questions:

1. What is your burning passion?

_____

_____

_____

2. What do you dream of accomplishing?

_____

_____

_____

3. What have you always dreamt of doing?

_____

_____

_____

4. What is your burning desire in life?

_____

_____

_____

5. What were you born to do?

_____

_____

_____

6. What work would make your life meaningful?

_____

_____

_____

(Continued on next page)

(Passions continued)

7. What things do you love doing so much that you would do them for free?

_____

_____

_____

8. What are your five most important values in life?

_____

_____

_____

9. What have you always wanted to do, but were afraid to try?

_____

_____

_____

10. If you won the lottery, what would you do with your time?

_____

_____

_____

11. With whom would you spend your time and where would you live?

_____

_____

_____

Nurturing Relationships

People with addictive personalities need to develop and maintain nurturing relationships. The following questions will help you to explore the quality of the relationships you have with significant people in your life.

Family

You get many of your day-to-day support and nurturing needs met through relationships with family members. In the chart below, identify members of your family and describe how these family members help you to meet your nurturing needs.

Family member	How he or she helps me meet my needs

Friends

You also get many of your day-to-day intimacy needs met through relationships with friends. In the chart below, identify friends and describe how they help you to meet your intimacy needs:

Friend	How he or she helps me meet my needs

© 2008 WHOLE PERSON ASSOCIATES, 210 WEST MICHIGAN ST., DULUTH MN 55802-1908 ▪ 800-247-6789

How I Get My *Highs*

People with addictive personalities OFTEN need to engage in exciting and often risky leisure activities. It is through these types of activities that you get your *high*. The following exercises have been developed to help you think about the activities in your life.

Where	What I do
In my personal life	
In my career	
In school	

About Your Risks

1. What types of risks do you tend to take most often?

_____

_____

_____

2. What types of risks do you need to take more often?

_____

_____

_____

3. Are there risks you should not continue to take?

_____

_____

_____

4. Are you taking the amount and types of risks you feel you should be taking? Why or why not?

_____

_____

_____

5. Are you taking too many of the wrong kinds of risks? Describe these risks.

_____

_____

_____

6. Are you taking too many foolish risks? Describe these risks.

_____

_____

_____

The Perfect Day

Write about how you would spend the perfect day?

_____

_____

_____

_____

_____

_____

_____

_____

_____

_____

What did you learn from what you wrote about above?

_____

_____

_____

_____

_____

_____

_____

_____

_____

_____

More Support

How can you start receiving more support from your current relationships?

Current Risk-Taking Behavior

Now write a statement that summarizes your current risk-taking behavior.

_____

_____

_____

_____

_____

_____

_____

_____

_____

_____

What changes would you like to make to your risk-taking behavior?

_____

_____

_____

_____

_____

_____

_____

_____

_____

_____

Stages of Addiction

Stage One: Internal Change

- Person experiences the high produced by certain objects or events
- Person experiences mood changes
- Addictive personality settles in place

Stage Two: Lifestyle Change

- Addictive behavior begins
- Behavioral dependency begins to develop
- Life and relationships are arranged and guided by addictive logic

Stage Three: Life Breakdown

- Addictive personality is in total control
- Life begins to break down
- Coping and interactions with others is difficult and filled with stress

Types of *Highs*

Following are a few of the *highs* people with addictive personalities crave:

- Alcoholic beverages
- Caffeinated beverages
- Gambling
- Internet addiction
- Overeating
- Porn addiction
- Prescription medications like Valium
- Sexual promiscuity
- Shopping
- Spending money
- Stealing and shoplifting
- Substances like heroin, marijuana
- Watching television
- Working too much

SECTION III:
Codependency Characteristics Scale

Name_____

Date_____

Codependency Characteristics Scale Directions

Many definitions are used to talk about codependency. The original definition of codependency simply referred to the types of responses and behaviors that people develop from living with a substance abuser. Over the years, however, the definition of codependency has expanded to include maladaptive, compulsive behaviors learned by family members in order to survive in a family with substance abusers. In these relationships, people become addicted to helping and enabling another person in order to distract them from meeting their own needs. Their happiness comes from helping and caring for others.

People experiencing codependency are overwhelmed by life and need stronger people to help them get through life. They feel that they cannot cope and that they are incapable of taking care of themselves. They feel they need to turn to other people for help. The Codependency Characteristics Scale measures how well you fulfill the normal responsibilities of adult life, identifies your feelings of inadequacy, and explores things that are lacking in your life.

The Codependency Characteristics Scale can help you identify, based on your personality, your approach to life. This scale contains 48 statements. Read each of the statements and decide how much you agree with the statement. In each of the choices listed, circle the number of your response on the line to the right of each statement.

In the following example, the circled **Like Me** indicates that the statement describes the person taking the assessment:

SECTION 1: CARETAKING

I often feel compelled to help people solve their problems   Not Like Me

This is not a test, and there are no right or wrong answers. Do not spend too much time thinking about your answers. Your initial response will likely be the most true for you.

Be sure to respond to every statement.

(Turn to the next page and begin)

Codependency Characteristics Scale

SECTION 1: CARETAKING

I often feel compelled to help people solve their problems	Like Me	Not Like Me
I feel responsible for others' needs, wants and well-being	Like Me	Not Like Me
I feel angry if my help is not effective	Like Me	Not Like Me
I tend to anticipate other people's needs	Like Me	Not Like Me
I feel best when I am giving to others	Like Me	Not Like Me
I find needy people attracted to me	Like Me	Not Like Me
I often say "yes" when I mean "no"	Like Me	Not Like Me
I need other people	Like Me	Not Like Me
I am not the only person I have to please	Like Me	Not Like Me
I do not feel capable of taking care of myself	Like Me	Not Like Me
I often feel bored and empty unless I am solving a crisis	Like Me	Not Like Me
I often feel bored and empty unless I am helping others	Like Me	Not Like Me
I try to control other people in my life	Like Me	Not Like Me
I often ignore my own needs in my desire to help others	Like Me	Not Like Me
I do things for people that they can do for themselves	Like Me	Not Like Me
I tend to overextend myself in caring for others	Like Me	Not Like Me

(Continued on the next page)

(Codependency Characteristics Scale continued)

SECTION 2: SELF-WORTH

I fear being rejected	Like Me	Not Like Me
I feel ashamed of who I am	Like Me	Not Like Me
I often wish good things would happen to me	Like Me	Not Like Me
I rarely push myself to see what I can achieve	Like Me	Not Like Me
I am a follower rather than a leader	Like Me	Not Like Me
I reject praise or compliments	Like Me	Not Like Me
I feel better when I know others are in charge	Like Me	Not Like Me
What other people say tends to bother me	Like Me	Not Like Me
I need other people to make me feel good	Like Me	Not Like Me
I often do not trust my own judgment	Like Me	Not Like Me
I usually blame myself for things that happen to me	Like Me	Not Like Me
I put myself down for how I think, feel and act	Like Me	Not Like Me
I feel as if I am not quite good enough	Like Me	Not Like Me
I tend to take things very personally	Like Me	Not Like Me
I cannot express who I really am	Like Me	Not Like Me
I achieve self-esteem by helping others solve their problems	Like Me	Not Like Me

(Continued on the next page)

(Codependency Characteristics Scale continued)

SECTION 3: DEPENDENCY

I care so much I sometimes hinder the recovery of others	Like Me	Not Like Me
I feel incomplete if I do not have someone special	Like Me	Not Like Me
I am not capable of getting along on my own	Like Me	Not Like Me
I do not like to make my own decisions	Like Me	Not Like Me
Other people can take care of me better than I can	Like Me	Not Like Me
I always ask for advice before making decisions	Like Me	Not Like Me
I always give in to others in an argument	Like Me	Not Like Me
I always like to be by myself	Like Me	Not Like Me
I find it difficult to cope well by myself	Like Me	Not Like Me
I often ask other people for guidance before beginning new tasks	Like Me	Not Like Me
I find it difficult to cope well by myself	Like Me	Not Like Me
I look for happiness outside myself	Like Me	Not Like Me
I desperately seek love and approval	Like Me	Not Like Me
I do not like to lose anyone who provides me with happiness	Like Me	Not Like Me
My relationships are my only source of good feelings	Like Me	Not Like Me
I do not want to do anything to make others angry at me	Like Me	Not Like Me

(Go to the Scoring Directions on the next page)

Codependency Characteristics Scale
Scoring Directions

The Codependency Characteristics Scale is designed to measure your tendencies to be codependent in your relationships with others. Although many characteristics are present in the lives of codependents, people who are codependent typically take caring for other people to the extreme, have a low sense of self-worth, and tend to be dependent on other people. These characteristics are prominent and make up the three scales for the Codependency Characteristics Scale: Caretaking, Self-Worth and Dependency. To score this scale:

1. Add the number of **Like Me** responses you circled in each of the three previous sections.

2. Then, transfer your totals for each of the three sections to the corresponding lines below:

Section 1: Caretaking Total   =   _____

Section 2: Self-Worth Total   =   _____

Section 3: Dependency Total =   _____

(Go to the next page to interpret your scores.)

© 2008 WHOLE PERSON ASSOCIATES, 210 WEST MICHIGAN ST., DULUTH MN 55802-1908 ▪ 800-247-6789

SECTION III: CODEPENDENCY CHARACTERISTICS SCALE

Codependency Characteristics Scale
Profile Interpretation

TOTAL INDIVIDUAL SCORES	RESULT	INDICATIONS
11 to 16	High	You have the beliefs and behaviors of someone who is codependent in that you are an extreme caretaker, have low self-esteem most of the time, and are very dependent on other people in your life.
6 to 10	Moderate	You have beliefs and behaviors similar to those of most other people. Moderate scores mean that you tend to believe that you are not necessarily codependent, but that at times you feel like you are an extreme caretaker, have low self-worth, and are somewhat dependent on other people.
0 to 5	Low	You do not have codependency beliefs and behaviors. You tend to care for people but not in an extreme way, have a good sense of self-esteem, and tend to be interdependent rather than dependent.

For scales which you scored in the **Moderate** or **High** range, find the descriptions on the pages that follow. Then, read the description and complete the exercises that are included. No matter how you scored, low, moderate or high, you will benefit from these exercises.

(Continued on the next page)

Codependency Characteristics Scale Descriptions

For any scales in which you scored in the MODERATE or HIGH ranges, find that description on the pages that follow. Read the description and complete the exercises that are included. These exercises will help you to overcome your tendencies toward codependency.

Scale I: CARETAKING

People scoring High on this scale feel that they are solely responsible for other people's needs, wants and demands. They somehow feel pulled and motivated to help others solve their problems. They always attempt to anticipate others' needs and desires and quickly act to satisfy them. They are very giving and thus attract needy people like a magnet. They need other people and do not like to be alone. Being around other people and helping them makes them feel better about themselves in general. They can become very controlling in their efforts to get their own needs met, so caretaking becomes an addiction to them.

Scale II: SELF-WORTH

People scoring High on this scale usually do not feel good about themselves. They are constantly afraid of being rejected by others and may even feel ashamed of who they are. They often wait for good things to happen to them and do not push themselves to achieve what they are capable of achieving. They tend to be followers rather than leaders. They are concerned about what other people say about them, and what others say often bothers them. They often do not trust their own judgment and allow others to make decisions for them.

Scale III: DEPENDENCY

People scoring High on this scale always want to please other people. They feel incomplete without a significant other in life because they cannot get by on their own. They look to others to make decisions for them and often to take care of them in general. They do not like being by themselves, and being with other people makes them feel better about themselves. They simply have trouble coping with life by themselves.

Codependency suggests that other people in the family of a substance abuser also suffer from their own addiction, in which they unintentionally effect and reinforce or enable the substance abuser. Regardless of your scores on the assessment, you can reduce your tendencies to be codependent by completing the exercises that follow.

Caretaking

Codependents usually feel an overwhelming motivation to care for other people. Complete the following chart to identify the people in your life that you feel you need to take care of.

People I take care of in my life	How I take care of them

Attachments

Most codependents are attached to people and problems in their environment. Attachment is defined as being overly-involved, even hopelessly entangled, with other people or their problems. Complete the following exercises to determine the amount of your attachment.

To what extent are you excessively worried about and preoccupied with a problem? What is it and why are you preoccupied with it?

_____

_____

_____

To what extent are you excessively worried about and preoccupied with a person? Who is it and why are you preoccupied with him or her?

_____

_____

_____

In what ways do you find yourself becoming obsessed with and controlling of the people and problems in your environment?

_____

_____

_____

Under what circumstances do you find yourself becoming emotionally dependent on the people around you? Who are these people?

_____

_____

_____

Under what circumstances do you find yourself being a caretaker or rescuer to people around you? To what people and why do you do it?

_____

_____

_____

With what people do you find yourself compelled, almost forced, to help them solve their problems?

_____

_____

_____

Low Self-Worth

Most codependents have a low sense of self-worth. Some of them often come from troubled, dysfunctional families, but tend to deny that their family was dysfunctional in any way. Some, on the other hand, will do just the opposite and re-enact the drama of childhood or end up with an addiction because it is very familiar to them. Complete the following statements:

I often reject compliments or praise because . . .

_____

_____

_____

_____

I often think I am not quite good enough because . . .

_____

_____

_____

_____

I feel different from the rest of the world because . . .

_____

_____

_____

_____

I am afraid to make mistakes because . . .

_____

_____

_____

_____

(Continued on the next page)

(Low Self-Worth continued)

I feel ashamed of who I am because . . .

_____

_____

_____

_____

I blame myself for everything that happens because . . .

_____

_____

_____

_____

I wish other people would love me because . . .

_____

_____

_____

_____

I feel frustrated when others do not change because . . .

_____

_____

_____

_____

Dependency

Codependents have boundary problems and desperately need boundaries in their lives. You need to set limits on what you do for others and what you will allow other people to do for you. Complete the following exercise to identify the boundaries that you need to set for yourself.

With whom I need to set new boundaries	Boundaries I will set with him / her
EXAMPLE: My husband	I will not allow my husband to physically abuse me any more.

Communication Skills

Most codependents have an ineffective communication style. Much of your language is intended to manipulate others, please others, and try to control others. Complete the following questions related to your communication style with other people:

List the times when you negate or minimize your thoughts or feelings:

_____

_____

_____

List the times you laugh when you want to cry:

_____

_____

_____

List the times you say you are okay, but you are not:

_____

_____

_____

List the times you react to others inappropriately:

_____

_____

_____

_____

List the times you need to be more assertive (asking for what you want without being aggressive or expressing anger):

_____

_____

_____

_____

(Continued on the next page)

(Communication Skills continued)

List the times you find yourself lying to others:

_____

_____

_____

_____

List the times you apologize when you do not need to:

_____

_____

_____

_____

List the times when you make excuses for other people:

_____

_____

_____

_____

List the times when you feel guilty or ashamed for the way you communicate with others:

_____

_____

_____

_____

List the times when you are worried about what other people think of you or how they are judging you:

_____

_____

_____

_____

'Responsibilities'

Write about why you think and feel responsible for other people's feelings, thoughts, actions, and well-being.

_____

_____

_____

_____

_____

_____

_____

_____

_____

_____

_____

Write about how your caretaking has impacted your life.

_____

_____

_____

_____

_____

_____

_____

_____

_____

_____

_____

Codependency

Now that you have completed the assessment, describe your codependency in the space below:

_____

_____

_____

_____

_____

_____

_____

_____

_____

_____

_____

_____

_____

_____

_____

_____

_____

_____

_____

_____

_____

_____

Irresponsible People

You possibly feel responsible for so much because people around you feel responsible for so little.

Who are these people and what would you like them to take responsibility for?

_____

_____

_____

_____

_____

_____

_____

_____

_____

_____

_____

_____

_____

_____

_____

_____

_____

_____

_____

_____

_____

_____

Codependency Patterns

Codependents typically engage in the following behaviors:

- They induce, often in subtle ways, the addict to become dependent on them.

- They also try to change or correct the addict and in doing so actually help facilitate the addiction.

- They validate their worth through their helping efforts.

- They base their happiness / well-being / worth on the recovery of their addicted loved one or on the happiness / well-being of others.

- They neglect their own needs in order to provide or care for others.

Codependent Characteristics

Codependents share some of the following common characteristics:

- Feel responsible for other people.

- Have low self-esteem and self-worth.

- Feel anxious and obsessed about problems and people.

- Are extremely controlling.

- Deny problems or pretend they are not happening.

- Are dependent on others for their happiness.

- Exhibit ineffective communication skills.

- Set weak boundaries with other people.

- Don't trust themselves or others.

- Often feel angry, hurt, or scared.

SECTION IV:
Relapse Warning Signs Scale

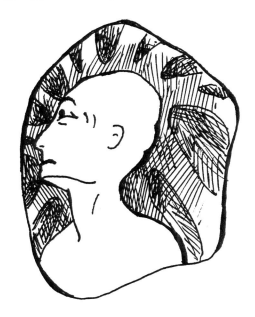

Name_____

Date_____

Relapse Warning Signs Scale Directions

Recovery consists of moving from the destructive effects of addiction to alcohol and other drugs to more healthy relationships, lifestyles and spirituality. Because recovery does not happen overnight and is a developmental process that occurs over time, you need to be vigilant about the warning signs that can help you to prevent a relapse. The Relapse Warning Signs Scale is designed to help you identify the changes in thinking, feeling and behavior that accompany relapse.

This scale contains 39 statements that are divided into three categories: Changes in Thinking, Changes in Feelings, and Changes in Behavior. Read each of the statements and decide whether or not the statement describes you. If the statement does describe you, circle the **YES** next to that item. If the statement does not describe you, circle the **NO** next to that item.

In the following example, the circled **YES** indicates the statement is descriptive of the person completing the scale.

I. CHANGES IN THINKING

I am having trouble thinking clearly   NO

This is not a test, and there are no right or wrong answers. Do not spend too much time thinking about your answers. Your initial response will likely be the most true for you.

Be sure to respond to every statement.

(Turn to the next page and begin)

Relapse Warning Signs Scale – Part I

I. CHANGES IN THINKING

I am having trouble thinking clearly	YES	NO
I am unable to solve simple problems	YES	NO
My mind often races and wanders	YES	NO
I am having trouble concentrating	YES	NO
I have been making bad decisions lately	YES	NO
At times I find it difficult to remember things	YES	NO
It is difficult for me to learn new information	YES	NO
I am getting confused more often and for longer periods	YES	NO
Sometimes I am not sure what is right or wrong	YES	NO
I easily get frustrated and irritable	YES	NO
I find myself losing my temper more often	YES	NO
Sometimes I just don't care about problems in my life	YES	NO
I have started to think alcohol or drug use will make me feel better	YES	NO

TOTAL = _____

(Continued on the next page)

(Relapse Warning Signs Scale continued)

Relapse Warning Signs Scale – Part II

II. CHANGES IN FEELINGS

I am having trouble controlling my emotions	YES	NO
I find myself overreacting emotionally	YES	NO
I sometimes find myself emotionally numb	YES	NO
I am starting to have "strange" feelings	YES	NO
I often have strong mood swings	YES	NO
I often try to ignore or hide my feelings	YES	NO
I have been feeling depressed and down	YES	NO
I sometimes feel helpless and powerless	YES	NO
I have started worrying about others more than myself	YES	NO
I have begun to feel like a failure	YES	NO
I sometimes experience periods of deep depression	YES	NO
Life often seems unmanageable to me	YES	NO
I get angry because I cannot act the way I want	YES	NO

TOTAL = _____

(Continued on the next page)

(Relapse Warning Signs Scale continued)

Relapse Warning Signs Scale – Part III

III. CHANGES IN BEHAVIOR

I do not have the energy I used to	YES	NO
I make plans which often fail	YES	NO
I am having more trouble dealing with stress	YES	NO
I have been either overeating or I eat very little	YES	NO
I have trouble getting things done	YES	NO
I am having trouble sleeping regularly	YES	NO
I am not able to follow through with plans I make	YES	NO
My daily routine has become irregular	YES	NO
I have started missing therapy and self-help groups	YES	NO
I find myself lying more often	YES	NO
I have trouble taking action when I need to	YES	NO
I impulsively do things without thinking first	YES	NO
I have been spending too much time alone	YES	NO

TOTAL = _____

(Go to the Scoring Directions on the next page)

Relapse Warning Signs Scale
Scoring Directions

The Relapse Warning Signs Scale is designed to help you determine if you are beginning to relapse into substance abuse. It identifies significant changes in your thinking, feelings, and behaviors. For each of the sections on the previous pages, count the number of YES answers you circled in each section. Put that number on the line marked 'TOTAL' at the end of each.

Transfer your totals to the spaces below:

CHANGES IN THINKING TOTAL   =   _____

CHANGES IN FEELINGS TOTAL   =   _____

CHANGES IN BEHAVIOR TOTAL   =   _____

Profile Interpretation

TOTAL INDIVIDUAL SCORES	RESULT	INDICATIONS
10 to 13	High	You are showing signs of relapsing back into substance abuse. You are experiencing major changes in your thoughts, feelings and actions.
5 to 9	Moderate	You may be starting to show signs of relapse. You are starting to experience major changes in your thoughts, feelings and actions.
0 to 4	Low	You tend not to be in danger of relapse. You do not seem to be experiencing any major changes in your thoughts, feelings or actions.

The Scales in which you scored in the "Moderate" and "High" ranges tend to be warning you about the possibility of a relapse. Now go to the next section for a description of each of the three Scales. Then complete the exercises that are included. No matter how you scored, low, moderate or high, you will benefit from these exercises.

Relapse Warning Signs Scale Descriptions

SCALE I — CHANGES IN THINKING includes a preoccupation with substances that can be abused, lack of clear thinking and poor decision making. These types of problems in your thinking can cause you to relapse or hinder your progress in recovery. Changes in thinking can come from a variety of self-defeating thoughts. People scoring Moderate or High on this Scale also begin to have problems concentrating on single topics, find learning new things very difficult, get confused more easily and more often, have trouble solving problems and remembering things, and find that their thinking begins to trigger feelings of frustration and depression.

SCALE II — CHANGES IN FEELINGS includes difficulty concentrating, sudden feelings of depression and a lower self-concept. These types of problems in feelings can cause you to relapse or to hinder your progress in recovery. People scoring Moderate or High on this Scale also begin to feel helpless over what happens in their lives, feel like a failure, have feelings of powerlessness in their jobs and their lives, over-react emotionally with others, work to hide their true feelings, have strong mood swings, suffer from periods of deep depression, and get angry and frustrated when they are unable to control their emotions and what happens in their lives.

SCALE III — CHANGES IN BEHAVIOR includes not having the same type of energy you used to have, not being able to deal effectively with stress anymore and having trouble doing small tasks. These types of problems in behavior can cause you to relapse or to hinder your progress in recovery. People scoring Moderate or High on this Scale also begin to have trouble sleeping regularly, do not eat a proper diet, have trouble following through on obligations, fail to follow through on plans, start keeping a very irregular schedule, begin to miss their therapy and self-help groups, find themselves lying to significant others more often, have trouble completing things, spend more time alone and start to act very impulsively.

The exercises that follow are designed to help you to explore the changes that are currently taking place in your thoughts, feelings and behaviors. You should complete the sections for which you scored in the Moderate or High ranges.

Changes in Your Thinking

The following questions are designed to help you explore changes in your thinking that might be leading to a relapse:

What is the primary warning sign of a change in your thinking that is worrying you?

_____

_____

_____

_____

_____

In what specific way has your thinking changed recently?

_____

_____

_____

_____

_____

As a result of these thoughts, you are . . .

_____

_____

_____

_____

_____

How are these thoughts setting you up for relapse?

_____

_____

_____

_____

_____

Changes in Your Feelings

The following questions are designed to help you explore changes in your feelings that might be leading to a relapse:

What is the primary warning sign of a change in your feelings that is worrying you?

_____

_____

_____

_____

_____

In what specific way have your feelings changed recently?

_____

_____

_____

_____

_____

As a result of these feelings, I am . . .

_____

_____

_____

_____

_____

How are these feelings setting you up for relapse?

_____

_____

_____

_____

_____

Changes in Your Behavior

The following questions are designed to help you explore changes in your behavior that might be leading to a relapse:

What is the primary warning sign of change in your behavior that is worrying you?

_____

_____

_____

_____

_____

In what specific ways has your behavior changed recently?

_____

_____

_____

_____

_____

As a result of these behaviors, I am....

_____

_____

_____

_____

_____

How are these behaviors setting you up for relapse?

_____

_____

_____

_____

_____

Life History

Many people who relapse into substance abuse have recurring life patterns from childhood that keep them from coping well. It is important that you understand the issues in your life as much as possible and attempt to identify the life patterns that may be setting you up for a relapse. Complete the following questions about your life and your attempts to cope with life problems. When you have answered all of the Life History questions, look for self-defeating patterns that keep reoccurring in your life.

How would you describe your mother and father?

_____

_____

_____

_____

_____

How would you describe your relationship with your parents?

_____

_____

_____

_____

_____

What negative experiences happened to you during your childhood?

_____

_____

_____

_____

_____

(Continued on the next page)

(Life History continued)

What types of substance abuse problems did your parents or other relatives have?

_____

_____

_____

_____

_____

What types of substance abuse problems did your friends and / or peer group have?

_____

_____

_____

_____

_____

How is your problem similar to that of your parents?

_____

_____

_____

_____

_____

How did the substance abuse problems of your parents affect you?

_____

_____

_____

_____

_____

Recovery Plan

Now that you have identified the primary relapse warning signs, you need to develop a recovery plan to assist you in managing your recovery. In addition to monitoring your thoughts, feelings and behaviors, you need to follow a recovery plan. This Recovery Plan will help you manage your recovery. Complete each of these four sections:

I. PROFESSIONAL COUNSELING

I am attending professional counseling   _____Yes   _____No

The greatest benefits of attending the sessions are . . .

_____

_____

_____

The reasons I have not been attending professional counseling are . . .

_____

_____

_____

II. STRESS MANAGEMENT TECHNIQUES

I am using stress management techniques   _____Yes   _____No

The greatest benefits of doing this are . . .

_____

_____

_____

The reasons I have not been using stress management techniques are . . .

_____

_____

_____

(Continued on the next page)

(Recovery Plan continued)

III. DIET AND HEALTH MANAGEMENT

I am eating a healthy diet   _____Yes   _____No

The greatest benefits of eating healthily, exercising regularly and getting enough sleep are . . .

_____

_____

_____

The reasons I have not been eating healthily, exercising regularly and getting enough sleep are . . .

_____

_____

_____

IV. SELF-HELP PROGRAMS

I am attending self-help programs regularly   _____Yes   _____No

The greatest benefits of attending these programs are . . .

_____

_____

_____

The reasons I have not been attending self-help sessions are . . .

_____

_____

_____

How Thinking Affects Potential Relapse

What have you learned about how your thinking affects a potential relapse?

_____

_____

_____

_____

_____

_____

_____

_____

_____

_____

_____

_____

_____

_____

_____

_____

_____

_____

_____

_____

_____

_____

_____

_____

_____

How Feelings Affect Potential Relapse

What have you learned about how your feelings affect a potential relapse?

_____

_____

_____

_____

_____

_____

_____

_____

_____

_____

_____

_____

_____

_____

_____

_____

_____

_____

_____

_____

_____

_____

_____

_____

How Behavior Affects Potential Relapse

What have you learned about how your behavior affects a potential relapse?

_____

_____

_____

_____

_____

_____

_____

_____

_____

_____

_____

_____

_____

_____

_____

_____

_____

_____

_____

_____

_____

_____

_____

Plan for Action

What action will you take to prevent relapsing?

_____

_____

_____

_____

_____

_____

_____

_____

_____

_____

_____

_____

_____

_____

_____

_____

_____

_____

_____

_____

_____

_____

_____

_____

_____

_____

Rewards of Recovery

- More control over your thoughts and actions

- Increased respect for yourself

- Increased trust in yourself and others

- Better relationships with others

- Better decision-making and problem-solving skills

- Greater ability to cope with problems

- Increased hope

- Increased chance for spiritual growth

- Increased physical, mental and emotional well-being

Facts About Recovery

Recovery is:

- A long-term process

- Very difficult

- The complete abstinence from substances

- Putting knowledge to work

- A set of tasks

- Being able to cope when you get stuck

100

SECTION V:

Substance Abuse Cessation Scale

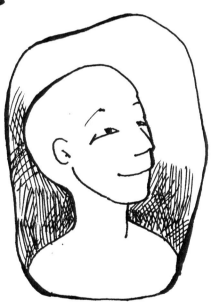

Name_____

Date_____

Substance Abuse Cessation Scale Directions

Most people realize when they have drug and alcohol problems. However, they often rationalize their substance abuse problems, create alibis, make excuses and simply repress unpleasant memories. They usually have reasons for continuing their abuse of substances. The Substance Abuse Cessation Scale is designed to get a clearer picture of the excuses that you may be using to continue your abuse of substances.

This scale contains statements divided into four categories. Read each of the statements and decide how descriptive the statement is of you. In each of the choices listed, circle the number of your response on the line to the right of each statement.

In the following example, the circled 1 indicates the statement is not at all descriptive of the person completing the inventory:

I. MENTAL	A Lot Like Me	Somewhat Like Me	A Little Like Me	Not Like Me
Drinking and / or drug use				
Helps me worry less	4	3	2	(1)

This is not a test and there are no right or wrong answers. Do not spend too much time thinking about your answers. Your initial response will likely be the most true for you. Be sure to respond to every statement.

(Turn to the next page and begin)

Substance Abuse Cessation Scale

I. MENTAL

Drinking and / or drug use	A Lot Like Me	Somewhat Like Me	A Little Like Me	Not Like Me
Helps me worry less	4	3	2	1
Relieves boredom in my life	4	3	2	1
Slows down life's hectic pace	4	3	2	1
Makes me more creative	4	3	2	1
Keeps me from obsessing about my problems	4	3	2	1
Stops little things from upsetting me	4	3	2	1
Helps me get through my day	4	3	2	1
Makes things bother me less	4	3	2	1

MENTAL TOTAL = _____

II. SOCIAL

Drinking and / or drug use	A Lot Like Me	Somewhat Like Me	A Little Like Me	Not Like Me
Makes me feel like part of the crowd	4	3	2	1
Helps me to celebrate better	4	3	2	1
Makes me more outgoing	4	3	2	1
Makes me close business deals more effectively	4	3	2	1
Is a normal part of my dinner	4	3	2	1
Makes me more fun at parties	4	3	2	1
Is part of my overall lifestyle	4	3	2	1
Make my accomplishments known to my supervisor	4	3	2	1

SOCIAL TOTAL = _____

(Continued on the next page)

(Substand Abuse Cessation Scale continued)

III. EMOTIONAL

Drinking and / or drug use	A Lot Like Me	Somewhat Like Me	A Little Like Me	Not Like Me
Relieves my sadness and depression	4	3	2	1
Makes me feel less lonely	4	3	2	1
Makes me feel more confident about myself	4	3	2	1
Makes me feel more grown up/younger	4	3	2	1
Gives me the courage to face life	4	3	2	1
Helps me to forget painful memories	4	3	2	1
Helps me to feel more intimate	4	3	2	1
Helps me feel more loving	4	3	2	1

EMOTIONAL TOTAL = _____

IV. PHYSICAL

Drinking and / or drug use	A Lot Like Me	Somewhat Like Me	A Little Like Me	Not Like Me
Helps me relax	4	3	2	1
Helps me fall asleep	4	3	2	1
Relieves chronic pain that I have	4	3	2	1
Makes food taste better	4	3	2	1
Stops my morning shakes	4	3	2	1
Puts me at ease talking with others	4	3	2	1
Simply tastes good to me	4	3	2	1
Gives me a high that I love	4	3	2	1

PHYSICAL TOTAL = _____

(Go to the Scoring Directions on the next page)

Substance Abuse Cessation Scale
Scoring Directions

People who are trying to quit using and abusing substances face four major types of roadblock: Mental, Social, Emotional, and Physical. The Substance Abuse Cessation Scale is designed to measure which roadblocks may be keeping you from quitting. For each of the four sections on the previous pages, count the scores you circled. Put that sum on the line marked "Total" at the end of each section.

Then, transfer your totals to the spaces below:

MENTAL ROADBLOCKS TOTAL   =   _____

SOCIAL ROADBLOCKS TOTAL   =   _____

EMOTIONAL ROADBLOCKS TOTAL   =   _____

PHYSICAL ROADBLOCKS TOTAL   =   _____

Profile Interpretation

TOTAL INDIVIDUAL SCORES	RESULT	INDICATIONS
25 to 32	High	You have many roadblocks that keep you from quitting the use of substances. You need to do much more to eliminate these roadblocks.
16 to 24	Moderate	You have some roadblocks keeping you from quitting the use of substances. You need to do more to eliminate these roadblocks.
8 to 15	Low	You do not have many roadblocks that keep you from quitting the use of substances.

For scales which you scored in the Moderate or High range, find the descriptions on the pages that follow. Then, read the description and complete the exercises that are included. No matter how you scored, Low, Moderate or High, you will benefit from these exercises.

Mental Roadblocks

People who are experiencing mental roadblocks continue to use and abuse substances because they believe that these substances help their mental state. When they are abusing substances, the world seems easier to manage. They believe that the substances relieve a lot of their stress and they tend to worry less. They also feel like the substances help them get through the day and prevent them from being upset about little things that go wrong in their lives. They believe that they are less bored and even more creative when using and abusing substances.

What are some negative beliefs you have about yourself?

_____

_____

_____

_____

_____

What types of things do you worry about?

_____

_____

_____

_____

_____

How do you believe that using substances helps you deal more effectively with your day-to-day stress?

_____

_____

_____

_____

_____

(Continued on the next page)

(Mental Roadblocks continued)

How does substance use make you more creative?

_____

_____

_____

_____

_____

What types of things could you do to cope without using substances?

_____

_____

_____

_____

_____

What substances help you cope the best (caffeine, tobacco, marijuana, etc)?

_____

_____

_____

_____

_____

What can you do to increase your mental alertness?

_____

_____

_____

_____

_____

(Mental Roadblocks continued)

PERMISSION-GIVING THOUGHTS

What permission-giving thoughts do you come up with to continue your addictions? Look at some of the examples listed below and some of the alternative thoughts that you could be saying to yourself.

Permission-Giving Thoughts	Alternative Thoughts
1. "I can handle one more drink."	1. "One more drink will lead to many. Don't do it."
2. "Nobody will know if I have just one more joint."	2. "I will know!"
3. "A drink will calm my nerves."	3. "Nervous is better than drunk. Find a better way to calm my nerves."
4. "People will think bad things about me."	4. "I am not worried about what other people think. If I do not want another drink, I will just say so."
5. "Everyone is drinking."	5. "Just because everyone else is doing something does not mean that I have to."

YOU TRY IT

Now you try it. In the first column list your thoughts that interfere with stopping your abuse of various substances. In the second column list some of the alternative thoughts that you can substitute for your permission-giving thoughts.

Permission-Giving Thoughts	Alternative Thoughts

Social Roadblocks

People who are experiencing social roadblocks continue to use and abuse substances because they believe that these substances make them more sociable. When they are abusing substances, they feel like they are more outgoing and fun to be around. They believe that other people like them more and that they can easily become part of the crowd. They believe that substances are a part of people's lives and that it is natural to use and abuse substances at home, with friends and in the workplace.

How do you show your interest in other people?

_____

_____

_____

_____

_____

_____

How are you cooperative with those around you?

_____

_____

_____

_____

_____

_____

How do you develop and maintain intimacy with others?

_____

_____

_____

_____

_____

_____

(Continued on the next page)

(Social Roadblocks continued)

In what ways do your communication skills hamper your ability to develop and maintain intimate relationships with others?

_____

_____

_____

_____

_____

_____

What interpersonal communication skills would you like to learn?

_____

_____

_____

_____

_____

_____

In what ways do you do things you do not like merely to be a part of the crowd?

_____

_____

_____

_____

_____

Emotional Roadblocks

People who are experiencing emotional roadblocks continue to use and abuse substances because they believe that these substances positively affect their emotions. When they are abusing substances, they are more confident in themselves and in their abilities. They are able to forget negative events that happened in the past, and face life more easily in the present. They believe substances help them feel less depressed and less lonely. They believe that the use of substances provides them with the courage they need to face life. They also believe that substances make them more loving and intimate in nature.

What are your limitations?

_____
_____
_____
_____
_____

How do you contribute to the world?

_____
_____
_____
_____
_____

What makes you happiest?

_____
_____
_____
_____
_____

(Continued on the next page)

(Emotional Roadblocks continued)

What emotions do you express well?

_____

_____

_____

_____

_____

What emotions do you have difficulty expressing?

_____

_____

_____

_____

_____

What do you love about yourself?

_____

_____

_____

_____

_____

What can you do to increase your emotional stability?

_____

_____

_____

_____

_____

Physical Roadblocks

People who are experiencing physical roadblocks continue to use and abuse substances because they believe that these substances help them physically. When they are abusing substances, they feel that when they are using, they can more easily talk to other people and the substances provide them with a natural high. They feel they help them to relax and fall asleep more easily at night. They believe that substances dull their chronic pain and any morning shakes they may be experiencing.

How do you protect your physical health?

_____

_____

_____

_____

_____

How do you maintain physical health through exercise?

_____

_____

_____

_____

_____

How do you maintain physical health through nutrition?

_____

_____

_____

_____

_____

(Continued on the next page)

(Physical Roadblocks continued)

How is substance abuse hurting your physical health?

_____
_____
_____
_____
_____

How does substance abuse control or relieve pain for you?

_____
_____
_____
_____
_____

How do you maintain physical health through sleep?

_____
_____
_____
_____
_____

How active is your lifestyle? Describe it. If your lifestyle is not active, why not?

_____
_____
_____
_____
_____

(Physical Roadblocks continued)

What types of physical activities would you like to begin?

_____

_____

_____

_____

_____

What can you do to increase your physical wellness?

_____

_____

_____

_____

_____

In what ways does substance abuse make you feel better physically?

_____

_____

_____

_____

_____

In what situations do you tend to use substances? What triggers this use?

_____

_____

_____

_____

_____

Primary Roadblocks

What are the primary roadblocks you want to overcome?

_____

_____

_____

_____

_____

_____

_____

_____

_____

_____

_____

_____

_____

_____

_____

_____

_____

_____

_____

_____

_____

_____

_____

_____

_____

Overcoming Roadblocks

What will you begin to do to overcome these roadblocks?

_____

_____

_____

_____

_____

_____

_____

_____

_____

_____

_____

_____

_____

_____

_____

_____

_____

_____

_____

_____

_____

_____

_____

_____

_____

_____

_____

_____

Roadblocks and You

What did you learn about yourself and roadblocks?
How will this information help you in the future?

_____

_____

_____

_____

_____

_____

_____

_____

_____

_____

_____

_____

_____

_____

_____

_____

_____

_____

_____

_____

_____

The Recovery Process Stages*

I. Transition – Giving up the need to control substance abuse.

II. Stabilization – Recovering from damage of substance abuse.

III. Early Recovery – Changes in thinking, feeling, and acting related to substance abuse.

IV. Middle Recovery – Repairing and maintaining a balanced lifestyle.

V. Late Recovery – Growing beyond the limitations of childhood.

VI. Maintenance – Balanced living and continued growth and development.

* Based on the book *Passages Through Recovery* by Terence T. Gorski, Published by Hazelden.

Continuum of Substance Abuse

- No Use

- Experimentation

- Occasional Use

- Regular Pattern Use

- Heavy Use

- Abuse

- Dependence

- Chaos